Dear God Kids®
at School

by Annie Fitzgerald

A LITTLE SIMON BOOK
PUBLISHED BY SIMON & SCHUSTER, INC., NEW YORK

Dear God,

DOES TWO PLUS TWO EQUAL FIVE?
AND WHAT IS THREE-TIMES-THREE?
I KNOW YOU KNOW THE ANSWERS,
SO CAN YOU PLEASE HELP ME?

Dear God,

If HISTORY IS THINGS
THaT HaPPeNeD IN THe PasT,
THeN oNe THING'S VeRY CLeaR To Me—
THaT YoU WeRe BUILT To LasT!

Dear God,

GEOGRAPHY IS HARD,
YOU SEE, I'M ONLY SEVEN.
COULD YOU PLEASE TELL ME JUST WHAT IS
THE WAY TO GET TO HEAVEN ?

Dear God,

When we do our writing,
I think I'm doing fine,
But somehow I can't get the letters
to sit on the line.

Dear God,

DO YOU THINK I'M CLEVER?
I TRY TO BE, IT'S TRUE.
BUT EVEN IF I'M GOOD AT MATH,
I STILL DEPEND ON YOU.

Dear God,

I THINK MY TEACHER'S NICE,
BUT THEN, WHY SHOULD IT BE,
WHEN I DON'T KNOW THE ANSWER,
SHE ALWAYS PICKS ON ME?

Dear God,

I like your name a lot—
I've learned to write each letter.
But there's one thing I have to ask—
Please make my writing better.

Dear God,

WHEN I DON'T LIKE MY LESSONS,
HOW NAUGHTY I CAN BE!
BUT IF I'M REALLY SORRY,
I HOPE YOU'LL STILL LOVE ME?

Dear God,

I've got my paintbox out,
to paint this pretty view.
Because you did it best of all
I think I'll copy you.

Dear God,

IT'S TIME FOR SCHOOL AGAIN,
THAT'S WHAT MY MOTHER SAID.
BUT THOUGH I LIKE MY TEACHER,
I'D RATHER STAY IN BED.

Dear GOD,

MY TeaCHER DREW THIS MaP
Of COUNTRIES NEAR AND FAR,
BUT OF aLL THE PLACES IN THE WORLD,
I WONDER WHERE **YOU** are ?

Dear God,

I've told my teacher
how terrific it would be
if you could sit beside me
and DO THE WORK FOR ME.

Dear God,

MY TeaCHeR TRIeS aND TRIeS
TO TeaCH Me HOW TO SPeL.
BUT aS YOU See FROM WHaT I RITe,
SHe DOSeNT DO SO WeL.

Dear God,

WERE YOU AT SCHOOL, LIKE ME,
WITH LOTS OF WORK TO DO ?
NOW YOU ARE GOOD AT EVERYTHING...
PERHAPS I WILL BE TOO !

Dear God,

NOW THAT I HAVE LEARNED TO WRITE,
I'M SENDING YOU A LETTER.
MY WRITING'S KIND OF SQUIGGLY,
BUT IS IT GETTING BETTER ?

Dear God,

We all got soaking wet
when we went out to play,
In all our prayers we asked for sun—
how come it rained today?

Dear God,

I Have To TeLL You
I THINK THaT SCHOOL IS fUN.
I'M TRYING TO DO MY LeSSONS,
PLease HeLP If I GO WRONG.

Dear GOD,

TODAY I THOUGHT I'D PAINT
ONE OF YOUR GIANT TREES—
BUT HOW YOU EVER MADE IT
JUST AMAZES ME!

Dear God,

Before we have our games,
I sometimes sit and dream.
You said you're always here with us,
so I know you're on our team.

This book was devised and produced by
Multimedia Publications (UK) Ltd.

Illustrations copyright © 1984 INTERCONTINENTAL GREETINGS LTD
Illustrations by Annie Fitzgerald
Text copyright © 1984 Roger Knights
This edition copyright © 1984 Multimedia Publications (UK) Ltd.
All rights reserved including the right of
reproduction in whole or in part in any form.

First published in the United States of America 1985 by
LITTLE SIMON, a division of Simon & Schuster, Inc.,
1230 Avenue of Americas, New York, New York 10020.
LITTLE SIMON and colophon are registered
trademarks of Simon & Schuster, Inc.

DEAR GOD KIDS is a registered trademark
of Intercontinental Greetings, New York.

ISBN 0-671-53034-8

Originated by D.S. Colour International Ltd.
Printed in Italy by New Interlitho.